PENGUIN BOOKS

There's no place like home

Penguin Books Australia Ltd,
487 Maroondah Highway, P.O. Box 257
Ringwood, Victoria, 3134, Australia
Penguin Books Ltd,
Harmondsworth, Middlesex, England
Penguin Books,
625 Madison Avenue, New York, N.Y. 10022, U.S.A.
Penguin Books Canada Ltd,
2801 John Street, Markham, Ontario, Canada
Penguin Books (N.Z.) Ltd,
182-190 Wairau Road, Auckland 10, New Zealand

First published by Penguin Books Australia, 1982

Copyright © Mary Leunig, 1982

Made and printed in Australia
by Hedges & Bell, Maryborough, Victoria

CIP

Leunig, Mary, 1950-.
There's no place like home.

ISBN 0 14 006443 5.

1. Australian wit and humor, Pictorial.
2. Caricatures and cartoons – Australia.
I. Title.

741.5'994

There's no place like home
drawings by
MARY LEUNIG

PENGUIN BOOKS

Mary Leunig

Mary Leunig.

Mary Leunig

Mary Leunig

I see . . . . .

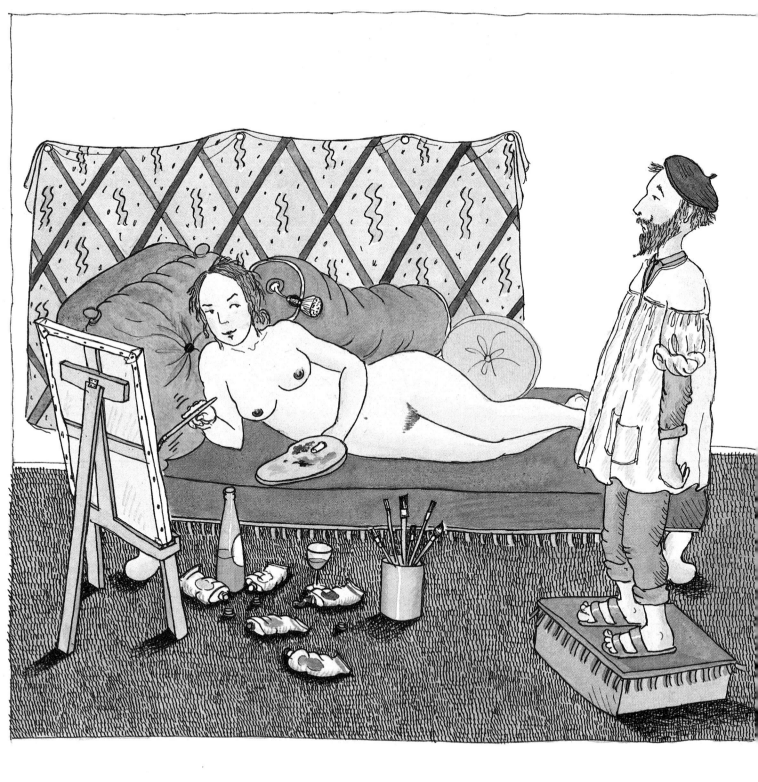